MY SERVANT JOSEPH

Words and Music by Kenneth Cope

TABLE OF CONTENTS

Copyright © 1993 Carpenter Music, BMI

Embryo Music
7210 South 900 East
Midvale, Utah 84047
(801) 566-6114

MY SERVANT JOSEPH
Words and Music by Kenneth Cope

Choir: Hum in unison one verse of PRAISE TO THE MAN (Hymn #27)

Reader 1: Praise to the man who communed with Jehovah! Jesus anointed that Prophet and Seer. We wish to speak this day of the Prophet Joseph Smith, but before we do, we must look further back through history.

Reader 2: Since the beginning of time, mortal men have been called upon from the heavens to be prophets and revelators to their fellow men, that God, through them, might make known His will to His children. For "Surely the Lord God will do nothing, but he revealeth his secret unto his servants the prophets."[1]

Reader 3: When Jesus Christ walked among men, He established a church built upon the foundation of revelation, and then called from among His earthly followers, apostles and prophets. These would receive revelation for the church when the Lord was no longer on the earth.

Reader 4: After the Lord's death and resurrection, the earthly church began to spread rapidly. And yet, it was only a matter of time before those in opposition to this new kingdom found a way to suppress it.

Reader 1: The apostles and prophets were slain for their testimony and the flow of divine revelation through the Savior's authorized servants came to an end. Consequently, the operation and teachings of the church were left to man's wisdom and therefore began to decay.

Reader 2: In the sixteenth century Martin Luther observed, "The spiritual powers [of the Church] have been not only corrupted . . . but absolutely destroyed . . . . Christianity has ceased to exist among those who should have preserved it."[2]

Reader 3: But how could it be otherwise? How could the church be led, if not by God? And what was man to do? Roger Williams, founder of the very first Baptist church in America, declared, "There is no . . . church on earth, nor any person qualified to administer any church ordinances; *nor can there be until new apostles are sent by the Great Head of the Church* for whose

---

[1] Amos 3:7.

[2] In Galat. (1535) Weins IX, P.I. 293, 24-27, p. 50; *Luther and His Times*, p. 509; *Martin Luther*, p. 188.

coming I am seeking."[3]

Reader 4: And Thomas Jefferson said this: "The religion builders have so distorted and deformed the doctrines of Jesus . . . [that I am] happy in the prospect of a restoration of primitive Christianity . . . ."[4]

Reader 1: *A restoration!* Such was the hope and anticipation of the true believer in Christ - that God would bring again His kingdom to the earth.

Song: THY KINGDOM COME - Choir

Reader 2: God *did* promise to restore the truth to mankind. And it was now His time to do so.

Reader 3: Joseph Smith was born in the year 1805, in the state of Vermont. While still a boy, his family relocated to upper-state New York. According to his mother, young Joseph was "much less inclined to the perusal of books than any of the rest of [the] children, but far more given to meditation and deep study."[5]

Reader 4: Joseph, speaking of that time, says, "My mind became seriously impressed with regard to . . . my immortal soul, which led me to searching the scriptures."[6] "From the age of twelve years to fifteen I pondered many things in my heart concerning the situation of the world . . . . My mind became exceedingly distressed for I became convicted of my sins . . . [and] by searching the scriptures, I found that . . . there was no society or denomination that built upon the gospel of Jesus Christ as recorded in the New Testament, and I felt to mourn for my own sins and for the sins of the world."[7]

Reader 1: While struggling under such conditions, Joseph read in the New Testament, in the book of James, these compelling words: "If any of you lack wisdom, let him ask of God, that giveth to all men liberally, and upbraideth not; and it shall be given him."[8] *"Never did any passage of scripture come with more power . . ."*

Joseph: (speaks overlapping with Reader 1 the words in italics)

---

[3] *Picturesque America*, p. 502, emphasis added.
[4] *Jefferson's Complete Works*, vol. 7, pp. 210, 257.
[5] Lucy Mack Smith, *History of Joseph Smith*, (Salt Lake City: Bookcraft, 1958), p. 82.
[6] Richard L. Bushman, *Joseph Smith and the Beginnings of Mormonism*, (Urbana and Chicago: University of Illinois Press, 1988), p. 53, spelling and punctuation revised.
[7] Ibid., p.55.
[8] James 1:5.

"Never did any passage of scripture come with more power to the heart of man than this did at this time to mine . . . . I reflected on it again and again, knowing that if any person needed wisdom from God, I did; for how to act I did not know, and unless I could get more wisdom than I then had, I would never know . . . . At length I came to the conclusion that I must . . . do as James directs, [and] ask of God. . . . So in accordance with this . . . I retired to the woods to make the attempt. It was on the morning of a beautiful, clear day, early in the spring of eighteen hundred and twenty. . . . After [going] to the place . . . [and] having looked around me, and finding myself alone, I kneeled down and began to offer up the desires of my heart to God. . . . [And while] exerting all my powers to call upon God . . . I saw a pillar of light exactly over my head, above the brightness of the sun, which descended gradually until it fell upon me. . . . When the light rested upon me I saw two Personages, whose brightness and glory defy all description, standing above me in the air. One of them spake unto me, calling me by name and said, pointing to the other, 'This is My Beloved Son. Hear Him!'"[9]

Reader 2: The Lord told Joseph many things, but in particular, that the world had turned aside from the gospel, so that His church and kingdom were no longer on the earth. Joseph was also promised that at some future time, the fulness of the gospel would be made known unto him.

Reader 3: The young prophet said that after his vision, his soul was filled with love and for many days he felt that the Lord was with him. And although great persecution followed him for saying he had seen a vision, yet he knew he could not deny it. He *had* seen the Lord, and this testimony would go with him to his death.

Joseph: "I [had] learned for myself . . . that a man who lacked wisdom might ask of God, and obtain . . . ."[10]

Song: LEARNING FOR MYSELF - Joseph

Reader 4: ". . . I the Lord, knowing the calamity which should come upon the inhabitants of the earth, called upon my servant Joseph Smith, Jun., and spake unto him from heaven . . ."[11] A prophet was again on the earth.

Reader 1: Upon meeting the Prophet Joseph for the first time, Amasa Lyman says, ". . . although there was nothing strange or different from other men in his

---

9 Joseph Smith-History 1:12-17.
10 Ibid., 1:20, 26.
11 Doctrine & Covenants, 1:17.

personal appearance, yet when he grasped my hand in that cordial way, . . . I felt as one of old in the presence of the Lord; my strength seemed to be gone, so that it required an effort . . . to stand on my feet; but in all this there was no fear, [for] the . . . voice of the Spirit whispered . . . that he was the man of God."[12]

Reader 2: Brigham Young, speaking of his introduction to Joseph Smith said, "We . . . repaired to the woods, where we found the Prophet . . . chopping and hauling wood. Here my joy was full at the privilege of shaking the hand of the Prophet of God, and receiving the sure testimony, by the spirit . . . that he was all that any man could believe him to be as a true prophet."[13]

Reader 3: Parley P. Pratt, commenting on the pleasure of his companionship with the Prophet, also says: "As we journeyed day after day, and generally lodged together, [Joseph and I] had much sweet communion concerning the things of God and the mysteries of His kingdom, and I received many . . . instructions which I shall never forget."[14]

Reader 4: Wherever the revelations given to Joseph were preached among men, they had their effect. And thus "mightily grew the word of God, or the seed sown by that extraordinary personage, the Prophet and Seer of the nineteenth century."[15]

Reader 1: "Thus saith the Lord God . . . A choice seer will I raise up . . . and unto him will I give a commandment that he shall do a work for . . . his brethren. And I will make him great in mine eyes . . . . and unto him will I give power to bring forth my word . . . . And out of weakness shall he be made strong . . . . And that seer will I bless, . . . and his name shall be called Joseph, and it shall be after the name of his father; and . . . the thing which [I] the Lord shall bring forth by his hand shall bring my people unto salvation."[16]

Song: MY SERVANT JOSEPH - Choir

Reader 2: The Prophet's life was filled with the work of the kingdom. The word of the Lord to Joseph was ". . . thou shalt devote all thy service in Zion; and in this thou shalt have strength." But the very next words of the revelation

---

[12] *Millennial Star*, vol. xxvii, p. 473.
[13] Ibid., vol. xxv, p. 439.
[14] *Autobiography of Parley P. Pratt*, (Salt Lake City: Deseret Book Co., 1970), p. 110.
[15] Ibid., p. 110.
[16] JST Genesis 50:27-33; 2 Nephi 3:7-15.

promised difficulty: "Be patient in afflictions, for thou shalt have many . . . ."[17]

Reader 3: Joseph and his wife Emma felt the awful weight of this prophecy in their family life. Their first three children died shortly after birth. They then adopted newborn twins, but ten months later one of the twins passed away as a result of exposure to the cold during an incident of mob violence. Nine children were born to Joseph and Emma, and two more were adopted, making eleven in all. Only five lived past childhood.

Joseph: " . . . in my leisure moments I have meditated upon the subject, and asked the question, why it is that infants, innocent children, are taken away from us . . . . The strongest reasons that present themselves to the mind are these: . . . . The Lord takes many away even in infancy, that they may escape . . . the sorrows and evils of this present world; they were too pure, too lovely, to live on earth; therefore, if rightly considered . . . we have reason to rejoice as they are delivered from evil, and we shall soon have them again."[18]

Reader 4: On one occasion, Joseph spoke at the funeral of his niece, Sophronia C. Smith. And " . . . pointing to the mother of [the] lifeless child, he said . . . '[Agnes,] you will have the joy, the pleasure, and satisfaction of nurturing this child, after its resurrection, until it reaches the full stature of its spirit.'"[19]

Joseph: " . . . when [a righteous] mother is deprived of the pleasure and joy of rearing her babe to manhood or womanhood in this life, through the hand of death, that privilege will be renewed to her hereafter, and she will enjoy it to a fuller fruition than it would be possible for her to do here."[20] Why? Because the Lord hath shown unto me " . . . that *all* children who die before they arrive at the years of accountability are *saved* in the celestial kingdom of heaven."[21]

Song: TINY HANDS - Emma and Joseph

Reader 1: What marvelous hope these truths gave to Joseph and Emma, that they might have their little ones again. What hope these wonderful truths give to us all! The Lord has indeed spoken again to man through His servant Joseph. Yet it was Joseph's desire that the Lord would speak to *all* men,

---

[17] Doctrine & Covenants 24:7-8.
[18] *History of the Church*, vol. 4, p. 553.
[19] Joseph F. Smith, *Gospel Doctrine*, (Salt Lake City: Deseret Book Co., 1977), p. 456.
[20] Ibid., p. 454.
[21] Doctrine & Covenants 137:10, emphasis added.

v

that they might *all* know Him as Joseph did.

Reader 2:   Even as Moses, Joseph wished "that [each of] the Lord's people were prophets"[22], "that *every* man might speak in the name of God the Lord."[23] This desire brought sorrow to Joseph as he reflected on the unbelief of mankind.

Joseph: "I was . . . introduced to a man from the east. After hearing my name, he remarked that I was nothing but a man, indicating by this expression that he had supposed that a person to whom the Lord should see fit to reveal his will, must be something more than a man. . . . Indeed, such is the darkness and ignorance of this generation, that they look upon it as incredible that a man should have any [communication] with his Maker."[24]

Reader 3:   Urging the church to greater faith, the Prophet said, ". . . God hath not revealed anything to Joseph, but what He will make known unto . . . even the least Saint . . . as fast as he is able to bear [it] . . . ."[25]

Joseph: ". . . it is your privilege to purify yourselves and come up to the same glory, and see for yourselves, and know for yourselves. Ask, and it shall be given you; seek, and ye shall find; knock, and it shall be opened unto you."[26]

Song: GO WITH ME - Joseph

Reader 4:   The Lord revealed these words to the Prophet: "I say unto my servant Joseph . . . you are my [friend] . . . . I [call] you [my servant] for the world's sake, and [you] are their [servant] for my sake."[27]

Reader 1:   How glorious! - the Master calling His servant His "friend"! And Joseph certainly remembered similar words of the Lord to His ancient apostles: "Ye are my friends . . . . Henceforth I call you not servants; for the servant knoweth not what his lord doeth: but . . . all things that I have heard of my Father I have made known unto you."[28]

Reader 2:   And yet, sobering were the words that followed: ". . . because ye are not of the world . . . the world *hateth* you. Remember . . . The servant is not greater than his lord. *If they have persecuted me, they will also persecute you* . . . ."[29]

---

[22]   Numbers 11:29.

[23]   Doctrine & Covenants 1:20, emphasis added.

[24]   Joseph Smith, *History of the Church*, vol. 2, p. 302.

[25]   Ibid., vol. 3, p. 380.

[26]   Ibid., vol. 1, p. 284.

[27]   Doctrine & Covenants 93:45-46.

[28]   John 15:14-15.

[29]   John 15:19-20, emphasis added.

Reader 3: And Joseph Smith *was* persecuted. He had to flee for his life from mobs, from threatened death, from state to state. And for what? *For his religion!* The Prophet willfully submitted to more than 45 slanderous lawsuits, yet nothing could be proven against his character. The wicked found fault with Joseph not because he was deserving of it, but because he was a virtuous man.

Reader 4: Brigham Young asked, "Did they hate [Joseph Smith] for his evil works? No. If he had been a liar, a swearer, a gambler, or in any way an evil doer, and of the world, it would have loved its own, and they would have embraced him . . . . If he had been a false prophet they never would have lifted a hand against him . . . ."[30]

Joseph: "Although I do wrong, I do not the wrongs that I am charged with doing; the wrong that I do is through the frailty of human nature, like other men."[31] "I never told you I was perfect; but there is no error in the revelations which I have taught. Must I then be thrown away as a thing of naught?"[32]

Reader 1: The adversary was aware that Joseph was destined to prove a disturber and an annoyer of his kingdom; else why should the powers of darkness combine against him?[33]

Joseph: "It has been the plan of the devil to hamper me and distress me from the beginning, to keep me from explaining myself to [the Saints]; and I never have [as yet] had opportunity to give them the plan that God has revealed to me . . . ."[34]

Reader 2: Since his first vision, the trouble came steadily with the exception of a few seasons of peace. And yet, whether in peace or in persecution, it was again his family who felt it the greatest. At times, it seemed that the very jaws of hell had opened the mouth wide after him as he was thrust from his loved ones by the sword, dragged to prison, and the enemies of truth prowled around him like wolves for his blood.

Reader 3: Meanwhile, his family could never be sure of his return. And so the moments of parting were the most trying of all.

Joseph: "When I entered my house, [my wife and children] clung to my garments,

---

[30] *Journal of Discourses*, vol. 1, p. 40; vol. 4, p. 78.
[31] *History of the Church*, vol. 5, p. 140.
[32] Ibid., vol. 6, p. 366.
[33] Joseph Smith—History 1:20.
[34] *History of the Church*, vol. 3, p. 286.

their eyes streaming with tears . . . . I requested to have a private interview with them a few minutes, but this privilege was denied me by the guard . . . . Who can realize the feelings which I [then] experienced . . . to be thus torn from my companion [and children], and leave [them] surrounded [by] monsters in the shape of men . . . . I felt overwhelmed . . . and could only recommend them to the care of that God whose kindness had followed me to the present time, and who alone could protect them, and deliver me from . . . my enemies, and restore me to my family."[35]

Reader 4: "If thou art called to pass through tribulation . . . know thou . . . that all these things shall give thee experience, and shall be for thy good."[36]

Song: GOING AS A LAMB - Joseph, Emma, Joseph III,
and women's choir

Reader 1: John Taylor recalls hearing the Prophet say, "God will feel after you, and He will take hold of you and wrench your very heart strings, and if you cannot stand it you will not be fit for an inheritance in the Celestial Kingdom of God."[37]

Reader 2: But why we ask? Why would God be so interested in our passing through difficulty?

Reader 3: Is it not to prove us; to see if we will serve Him at all costs?

Reader 4: Is it not to increase our faith in Him as He comes to our deliverance?

Reader 1: And is it not also that we, through tribulation, might obtain the knowledge necessary to help others who pass through similar difficulty?

Joseph: ". . . after having been enclosed in the walls of a prison for five months . . . . It seems to me that my heart will always be more tender . . . than [it ever] was before. . . . I think I never could have felt as I now do, if I had not suffered the wrongs that I have suffered."[38]

Reader 2: Joseph saw that through tribulation, he was more able to give help to those in need, and this only added to his appreciation for the Savior.

Joseph: "The Son of Man hath descended below . . . *all* [things]."[39] "He [was]

[35] *History of the Church*, vol. 3, p. 193.
[36] Doctrine & Covenants 122:5-7.
[37] *Journal of Discourses*, vol. 24, p. 197.
[38] *History of the Church*, vol. 3, p. 286.
[39] Doctrine & Covenants 122:8, emphasis added.

despised and rejected of men; a man of sorrows, and acquainted with grief ...."[40] ".... he [has suffered] pains and afflictions and temptations of *every* kind .... that his bowels may be filled with mercy, ... that he may know ... how to succor his people according to their infirmities."[41]

Reader 3: Joseph knew that the Lord understood him, and it was to the Lord that he turned for help.

Song: MAN OF SORROWS - Joseph

Reader 4: The Prophet once told a friend, "Oh, I am so tired that I often feel to long for my day of rest .... if I were on the other side of the veil I could do many times more for my friends than I can do while I am with them here. If it were not for the love of you, my brethren and sisters, death would be sweet to me as honey."[42]

Reader 1: On another occasion he said, "I do not regard my own life. I am ready to be offered a sacrifice for this people; for what can our enemies do? Only kill the body, and their power is then at an end. ... I love you with all my heart. Greater love hath no man, than that he should lay down his life for his friends. You have stood by me in the hour of trouble, and I am willing to sacrifice my life for your preservation."[43]

Reader 2: Joseph loved the Saints. He would die for them! But he also had a work to do and he knew that God would protect him until that work was done.

Joseph: "I yet live, ... therefore God requires more at my hands."[44] "God Almighty is my shield; and what can man do if God is my friend?[45] "... the world ... never will have power to kill me till my work is accomplished, and I am ready to die."[46] "... then I shall be offered freely."[47]

Reader 3: Just before his death, Joseph found himself surrounded by a group of military officers who confessed that he did not appear to be the evil man that his enemies had said he was. "But," they continued, "we cannot see what is in your heart, [nor] tell what are your intentions." To which the

---

[40] Mosiah 14:3.
[41] Alma 7:11-12, emphasis added.
[42] Truman Madsen, *Joseph Smith the Prophet*, (Salt Lake City: Bookcraft, 1989), p. 61.
[43] *History of the Church*, vol. 6, p. 500.
[44] Ibid., vol. 2, p. 308.
[45] Ibid., vol. 5, p. 259.
[46] Ibid., vol. 6, p. 58.
[47] Ibid., vol. 5, p. 259.

Prophet replied, "Very true, gentlemen, you cannot see what is in my heart, . . . but I can see what is in your hearts, and will tell you what I see. I can see that you thirst for blood and nothing but my blood will satisfy you."[48] Two days later, his blood was spilt!

Reader 4:   And while there were those among the Saints who would betray him, most of his brethren would stand by him to the death. One of these was his dear brother Hyrum.

Joseph: ". . . I could pray in my heart that all my brethren were like unto my beloved brother Hyrum, who possesses . . . the meekness and humility of Christ; and I love him with that love that is stronger than death . . . ."[49] ". . . Hyrum, what a faithful heart you have got! . . . [what] care you have had for my soul! O how many are the sorrows we have shared together; and again we find ourselves . . . [in the] hand of oppression."[50] "I advised my brother Hyrum to take his family . . . and go . . . . [for if we were] ever taken again, we [would] be massacred . . . . I want Hyrum to live . . . but he is determined not to leave me."[51] "I fear not death; my work is done. Keep the faith and I will die for Nauvoo."[52]

Song: BROTHERS - Joseph and Hyrum

(Begin the following shortly after the start of the instrumental postlude of *Brothers*.)

Reader 1:   In Carthage, Illinois, on the 27th of June, 1844, just after five o'clock in the evening, an armed mob--faces painted black--numbering from 150 to 200 persons, rushed the jail where Joseph and Hyrum were being held, climbed the stairs to the second story landing, and began to fire their guns through the door. Hyrum was shot first and fell calmly, exclaiming: "I am a dead man!"[53]

Reader 2:   John Taylor was the next to be shot, receiving four brutal wounds; and yet was miraculously spared by the hand of God to live through the massacre. Willard Richards, the only other person in the room, escaped the shower of gunfire virtually unscathed, literally fulfilling a prophecy made by Joseph over a year previously - that the time would come when gunfire would fly around Brother Richards like hail, and he should see his friends fall on the

---

[48]   *History of the Church*, vol. 6, p. 566.
[49]   Ibid., vol. 2, p. 338.
[50]   Ibid., vol. 5, pp. 107-08.
[51]   Ibid., vol. 6, pp. 520, 546.
[52]   Dan Jones, *The Martyrdom of Joseph and Hyrum Smith*, p. 3.
[53]   Doctrine & Covenants 135:1.

right and on the left, but he should not receive so much as even a hole in his garment.[54]

Reader 3:   The Prophet Joseph, seeing there was no safety in the room, and no doubt thinking that it would save the lives of his brethren if he could get out, turned calmly and attempted to leap from the window. Two shots pierced him from the door, and one entered his right breast from outside. He fell out of the window exclaiming, "Oh Lord, my God!" He landed on his left side a dead man.[55]

(Before continuing to read, wait until the instrumental postlude of *Brothers* has ended.)

Reader 4:   The rest of the Twelve Apostles, doing missionary work in the east, reported feeling terribly sad on that fateful day though completely unaware of the massacre that had just occurred.

Reader 1:   Brigham Young and Wilford Woodruff described themselves as being "very sorrowful, and depressed in spirits, without knowing the cause." Heber C. Kimball said he "felt very mournful as though he had lost some friend."[56]

Reader 2:   Orson Hyde went off alone, ". . . and walked the floor; tears ran down his face . . . ." He said he had ". . . never felt so before, and knew no reason why he should feel so then."

Reader 3:   George A. Smith felt "unusually cast down" and although calling upon the Lord for relief, he said none ever came. He went to bed but could not sleep. "Once it seemed to him that some fiend whispered in his ear, 'Joseph and Hyrum are dead; ain't you glad of it?'"[57]

Reader 4:   Joseph and Hyrum *were* dead! "In life they were not divided, . . . in death they were not separated!"[58] News arrived in Nauvoo at daylight the next morning. Around two-thirty in the afternoon, two wagons carrying the martyrs came into town, and nearly all of the citizens of Nauvoo gathered together to follow them to the Mansion House.

Reader 1:   After the bodies of the murdered brothers were cleansed and dressed in burial clothes, the immediate families were permitted to see them. Joseph's wife, Emma, "on first seeing the corpse of her husband . . .

---

[54]   *History of the Church*, vol. 6, p. 619.
[55]   Ibid., vol. 6, pp. 617-19.
[56]   Ibid., vol. 7, p. 132.
[57]   Ibid., vol. 7, pp. 132-133.
[58]   Doctrine & Covenants 135:3.

screamed and fell back, but was caught and supported . . . . She then fell forward to the Prophet's face and kissed him, calling him by name, and begged him to speak to her . . . . "[59] Almost in a state of insensibility she had to be carried back to her room. "Her oldest son, [Joseph III] approached the corpse and dropped upon his knees, and laying his cheek against his father's, and kissing him, exclaimed, 'Oh, my father! my father!'"[60]

Reader 2:   Lucy Smith, Joseph's and Hyrum's mother, wrote of her experience as follows: "I had for a long time braced every nerve, roused every energy of my soul and called upon God to strengthen me, but when I entered the room and saw my murdered sons extended both at once before my eyes and heard the sobs and groans of my family and the cries of 'Father! Husband! Brothers!' from the lips of their wives, children, brothers and sisters, it was too much; I sank back, crying to the Lord in the agony of my soul, 'My God, my God, why hast thou forsaken this family!' A voice replied, 'I have taken them to myself, that they might have rest.' . . . As . . . I arose again . . . [and looking] upon their peaceful, smiling countenances, I seemed almost to hear them say, 'Mother, weep not for us, we have overcome the world by love; we carried to them the gospel, that their souls might be saved; they slew us for our testimony, and thus placed us beyond their power . . . ours is an eternal triumph.'"[61]

Reader 3:   While the Saints were in mourning, a thirteen year old girl by the name of Mary Ann Broomhead cut her long hair, took the individual strands, and with a sewing needle stitched in fabric the following words:

"Sacred to the Memory of Joseph, and Hyrum Smith
who fell, as Martyrs, for the Gospel, of Jesus Christ.

. . . Zion's noblest sons are weeping;
See her daughters bathed in tears,
Where the prophets now are sleeping,
Nature's sleep - the sleep of years;
When the earth shall be restored,
They will come with Christ the Lord."[62]

Reader 4:   John Taylor expressed his grief this way: "Why must the good perish, and the virtuous be destroyed? Why must God's nobility, the salt of the earth,

---

[59]   *History of the Church*, vol. 6, p. 627.

[60]   Lucy Mack Smith, *History of Joseph Smith*, (Salt Lake City: Bookcraft, 1958), p. 325.

[61]   Ibid., pp. 324-25.

[62]   Found on display in the Museum of Church History and Art.

the most exalted of the human family . . . fall victims to the cruel, fiendish hate of incarnate devils?"[63] Alas, why?

Song: WHY MUST THE GOOD DIE / FREE AT LAST - Choir & Joseph

Reader 1:   "Hail to the Prophet, ascended to heaven!
Traitors and tyrants now fight him in vain.
Mingling with Gods, he can plan for his brethren;
Death cannot conquer the hero again."[64]

Reader 2:   "Joseph Smith, the Prophet and Seer of the Lord, has done more, save Jesus only, for the salvation of men in this world, than any other man that ever lived in it."[65]

Reader 3:   The Lord Himself testified, ". . . I did call upon [Joseph Smith] by mine angels, . . . and by mine own voice out of the heavens, to bring forth my work; Which foundation he did lay, and was faithful; and I took him to myself. Many have marveled because of his death; but it was needful that he should seal his testimony with his blood, that he might be honored and the wicked might be condemned."[66]

Reader 4:   Brigham Young declared, "I feel like shouting hallelujah, all the time, when I think that I ever knew Joseph Smith, the Prophet . . . . He was God's servant . . . . He . . . prepared the way for the people to walk in, and no [one] should be deprived of going into the presence of the Father and the Son . . . if they would walk in the path he had pointed out."[67]

Reader 1:   "He lived great, and he died great in the eyes of God and his people . . . ."[68] And while we reverence Joseph Smith for his greatness, the Latter-day Saints have never proclaimed that he was anything more than a prophet given to them of the Lord.

Reader 2:   Joseph was asked on more than a few occasions, "Do you 'Joe' Smith profess to be Jesus Christ?" To which the Prophet replied, "No, but *I profess to be His brother, as all other Saints* . . .

Joseph: (speaks overlapping with Reader 2 the words in italics)

---

[63]   B. H. Roberts, *Life of John Taylor*, (Salt Lake City: Bookcraft, 1989), p. 141.

[64]   *Hymns of the Church of Jesus Christ of Latter-day Saints*, (Salt Lake City: 1985), #27.

[65]   Doctrine & Covenants 135:3.

[66]   Ibid., 136:37-39.

[67]   *Journal of Discourses*, vol 3, p. 51; vol. 4, p. 297; vol. 1, p. 132.

[68]   Doctrine & Covenants 135:3.

"... *I profess to be His brother, as all other Saints* have done and now do."[69] "... [for Jesus] stretched forth his hand toward his disciples, and said, Behold ... my brethren! For whosoever shall do the will of my Father which is in heaven, the same is my brother, and sister, and mother."[70]

"If [we] wish to go where God is, [we] must be like God .... Search your hearts, and see if you are like God. I have searched mine, and feel to repent of all my sins."[71] "The nearer we get to our heavenly Father, the more we are disposed to look with compassion on perishing souls; we feel that we want to take them upon our shoulders, and cast their sins behind our backs."[72] "[Fellow Saints, we] ... must enlarge [our] souls towards each other, if [we] would do like Jesus, and carry [our] fellow-creatures to Abraham's bosom."[73] "[We must] feed the hungry, ... clothe the naked, ... provide for the widow, ... dry up the tear of the orphan, ... [and] comfort the afflicted, whether in this church, or in any other, or in no church at all, wherever [we find] them."[74] "We don't ask any people to throw away any good they have got; we only ask them to come and get more."[75] "I hope the Lord will grant that I may see you all again, and above all that we may overcome, and sit down together in the kingdom of our Father."[76]

Reader 3:   The Lord hath said, "... I have sent forth the fulness of my gospel by the hand of my servant Joseph ..."[77] "... Wherefore ... give heed unto all his words ... For his word ye shall receive, as if from mine own mouth ...."[78]

Reader 4:   And again, Jesus saith, "... If thou wilt be perfect, ... come and follow me."[79]

Song: COME, FOLLOW ME - Choir

---

69   *History of the Church*, vol. 3, pp. 29-30.
70   Matthew 12:49-50.
71   *History of the Church*, vol. 4, p. 588.
72   Ibid., vol. 5, p. 24.
73   Ibid., vol. 4, p. 606.
74   *Times and Seasons*, 15 Mar. 1842, p. 732.
75   *History of the Church*, vol. 5, p. 259.
76   Ibid., vol. 1, pp. 442-43.
77   Doctrine & Covenants 35:17.
78   Ibid., 21:4-5.
79   Matthew 19:21.

THY KINGDOM COME

Arranged by
RANDY KARTCHNER

Words and Music by
KENNETH COPE

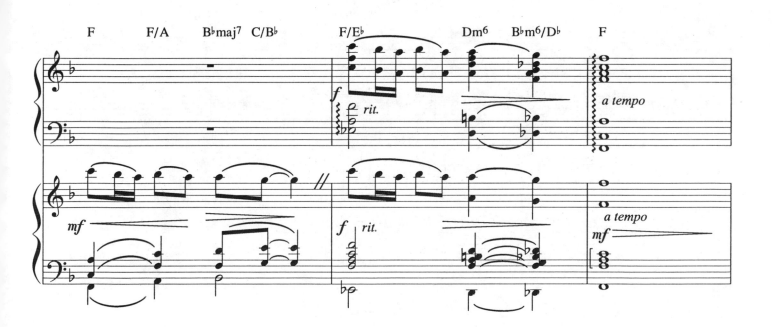

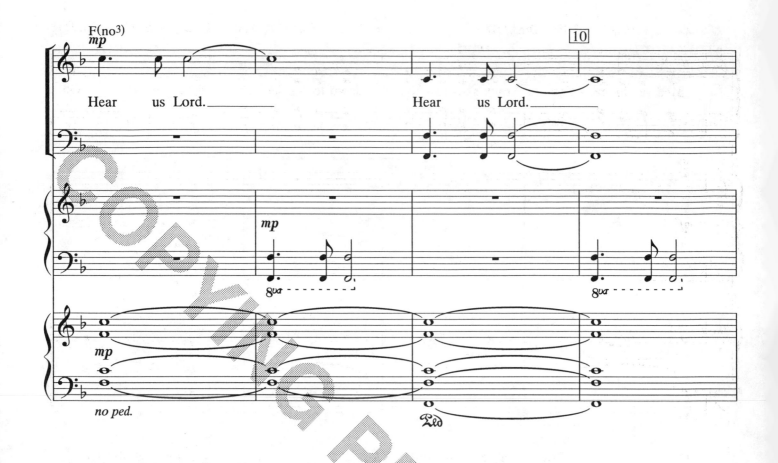

3

8

9

LEARNING FOR MYSELF

Arranged by
RANDY KARTCHNER

Words and Music by
KENNETH COPE

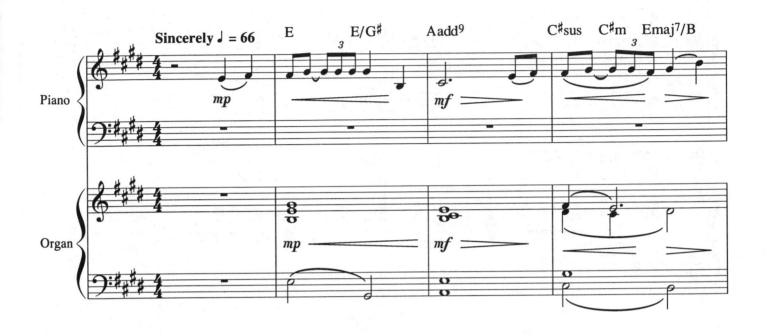

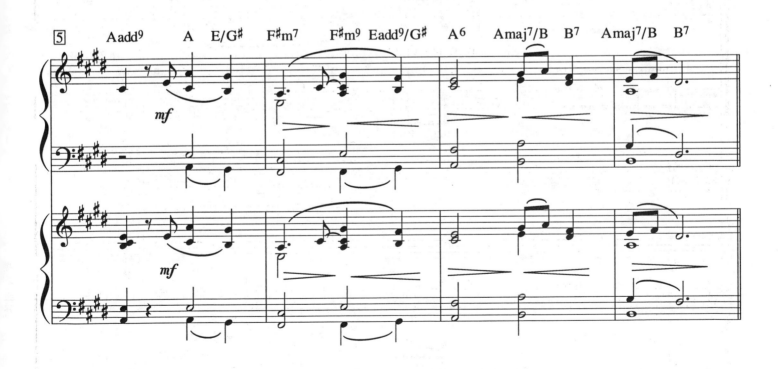

11

1. Young - er and so un - sure.____ Where could I turn to
2. Then how it came to me,____ I heard the words of

find my way? And the wit - ness I thirst - ed for, could I ob -
long a - go: "Ask him and you'll____ re - ceive," and now I can say.

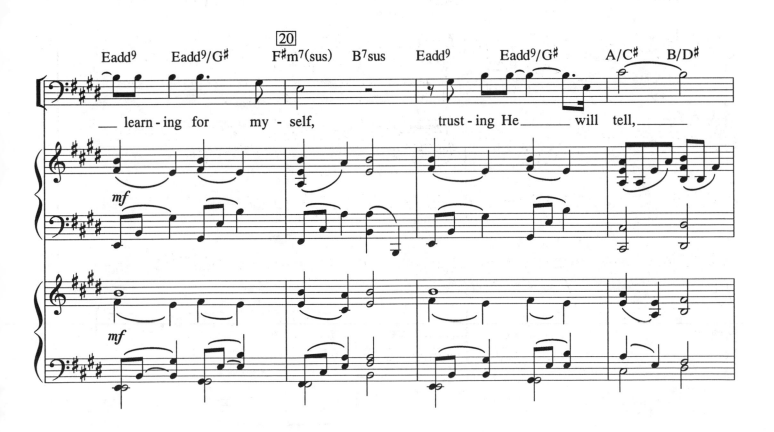

13

doubt-ing no more,___ learn - ing for my - self.

3. There are those who___ de - ny___ my word,___ they re-

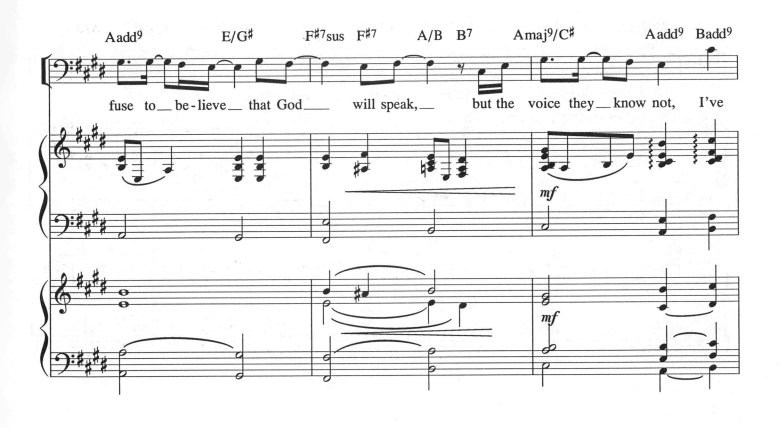

fuse to __ be-lieve __ that God __ will speak, __ but the voice they __ know not, I've

heard. I've felt __ His will for __ me. __ I'm __

15

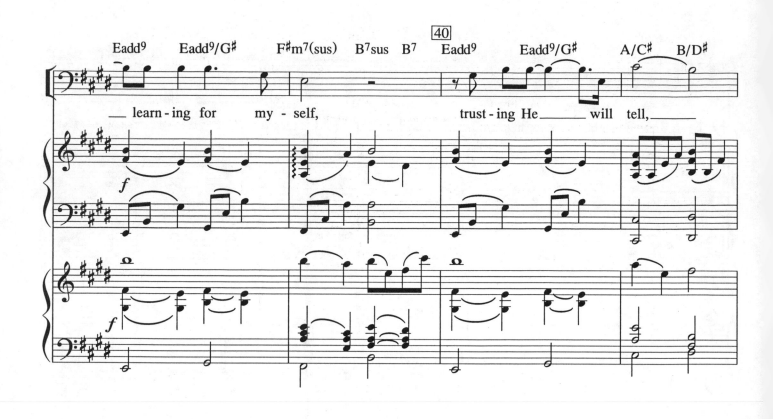

learn-ing for my-self, trust-ing He will tell,

doubt-ing no more, learn-ing for my-self.

He   is the sur - est way.   To   know   of Him, __

go   to __ Him,   for   He   speaks to those __ who be - lieve, __

and I_____ be - lieve, so He___keeps___ lead - ing___

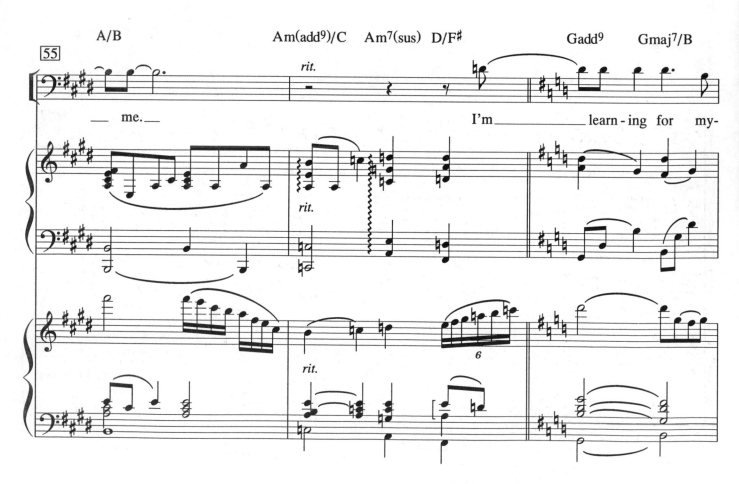

___ me.___ I'm_____ learn - ing for my-

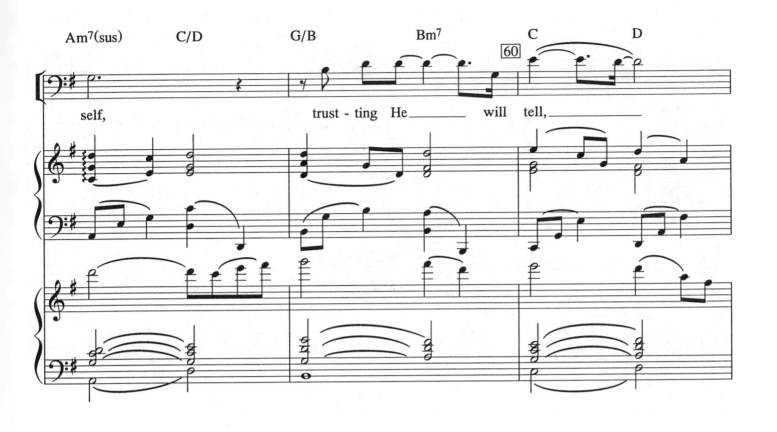

19

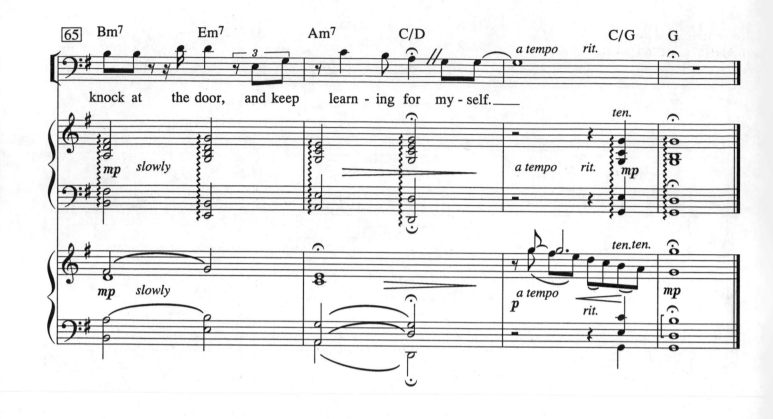

knock at the door, and keep learn - ing for my - self.___

MY SERVANT JOSEPH

Arranged by
RANDY KARTCHNER

Words and Music by
KENNETH COPE

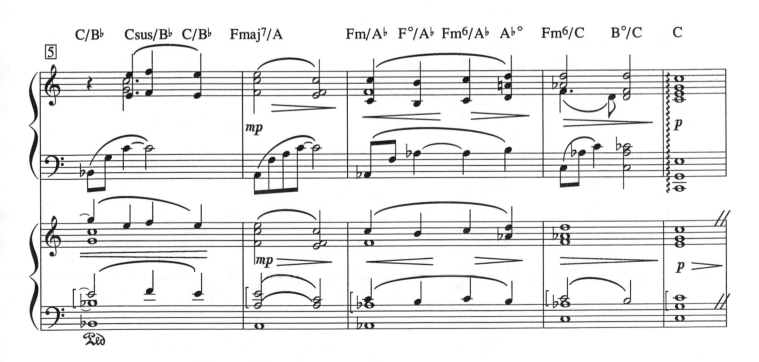

22

23

The voice of the Lord is un-to ev-ery na - tion.

All must an - swer, none shall es - cape.

26

29

my serv - ant Jo - seph.

TINY HANDS

Arranged by
RANDY KARTCHNER

Words and Music by
KENNETH COPE

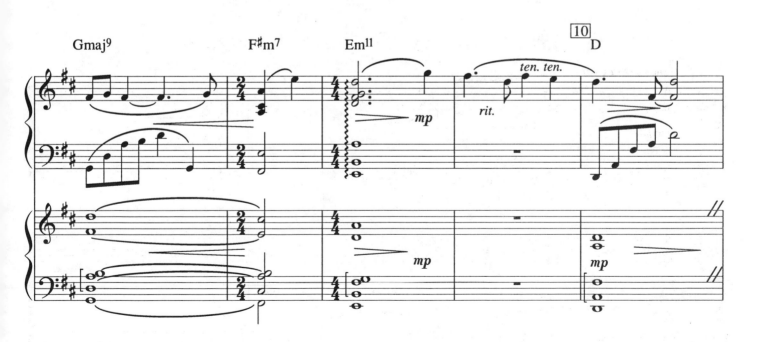

* All of verse 2, until the 2nd ending is the male part, and should be sung one octave lower than written. Beginning with the 2nd ending, sing as written.

wake, an-oth-er_ day._____ Oh God of heav'n,_ come guard this bed,_ and
mo-ment, and then set_ free._____ Oh God of heav'n,_ take hate from man, till

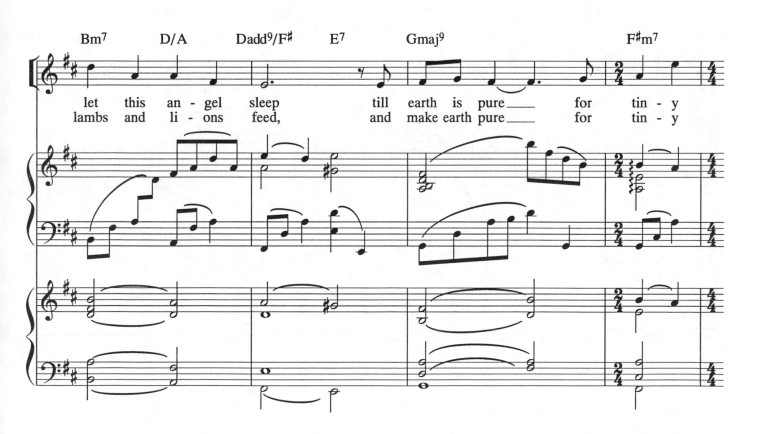

let this an-gel sleep till earth is pure___ for tin-y
lambs and li-ons feed, and make earth pure___ for tin-y

34

35

God of heav'n, ___ send Christ a-gain, ___ bring in His reign of

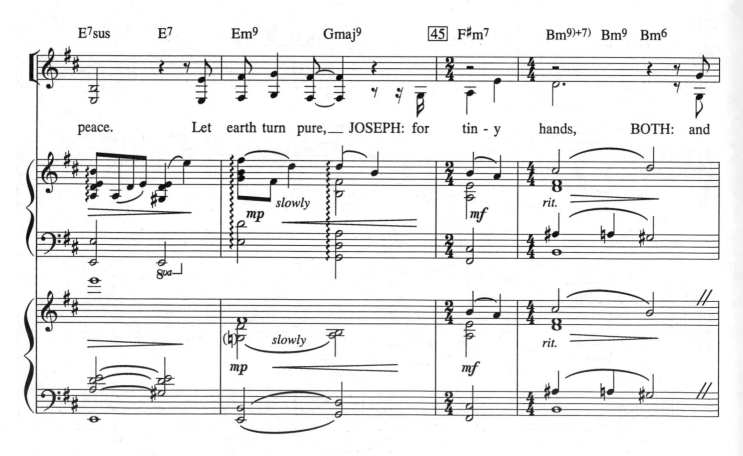

peace. Let earth turn pure, ___ JOSEPH: for tin-y hands, BOTH: and

GO WITH ME

Arranged by
RANDY KARTCHNER

Words and Music by
KENNETH COPE

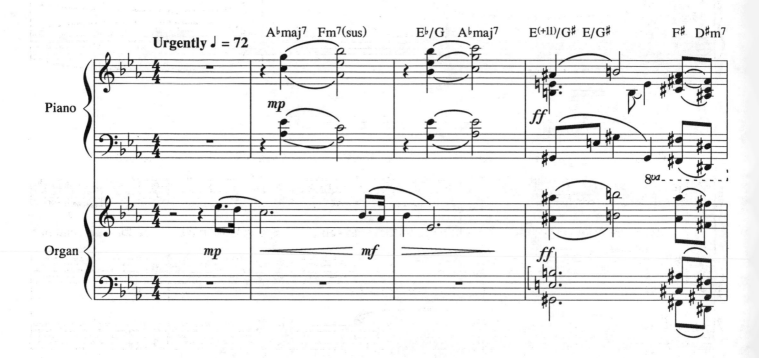

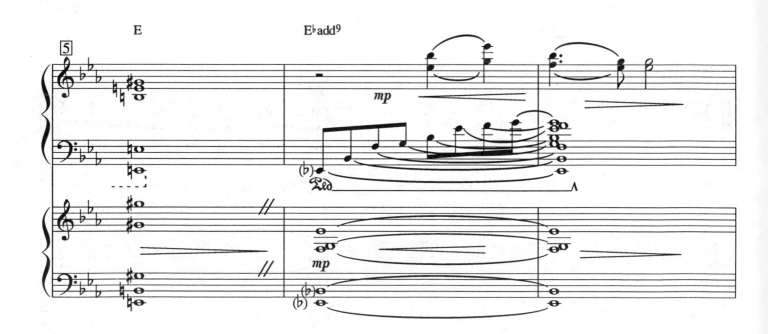

39

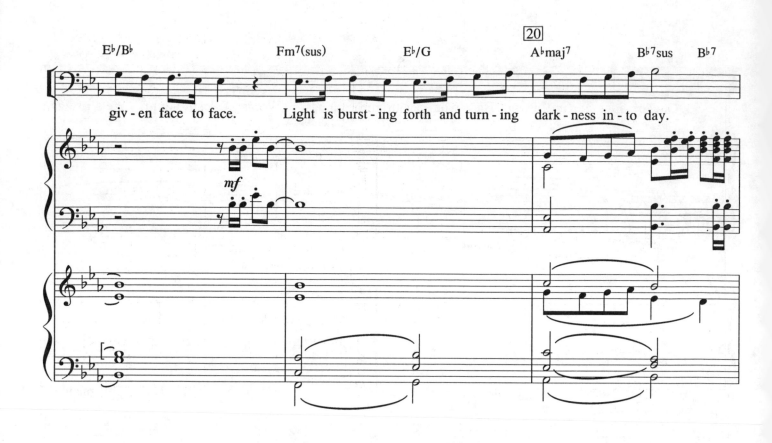

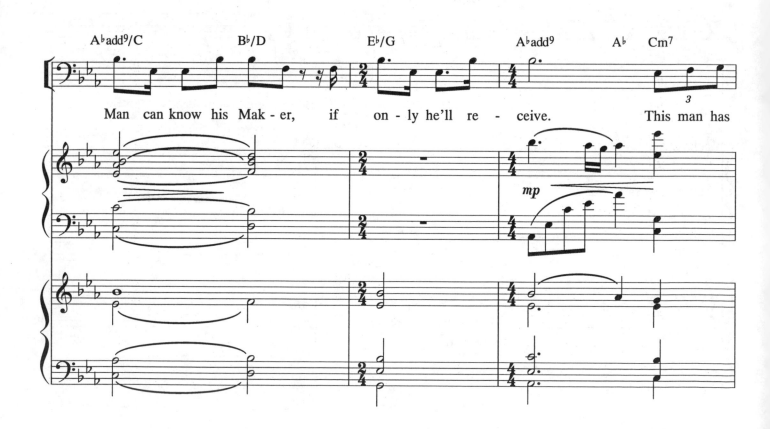

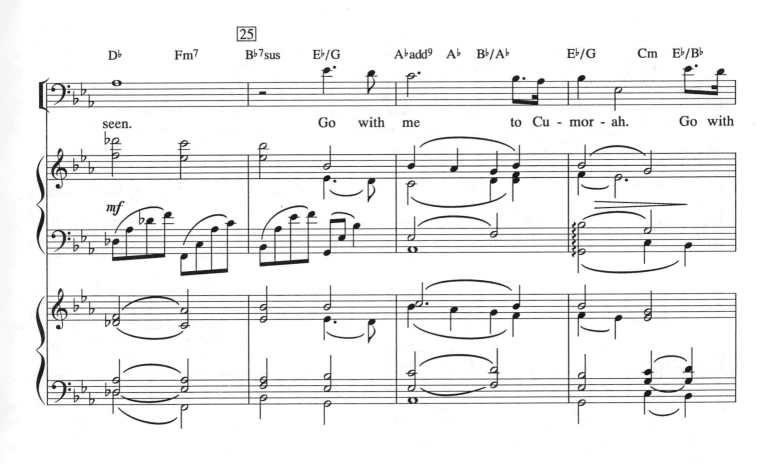

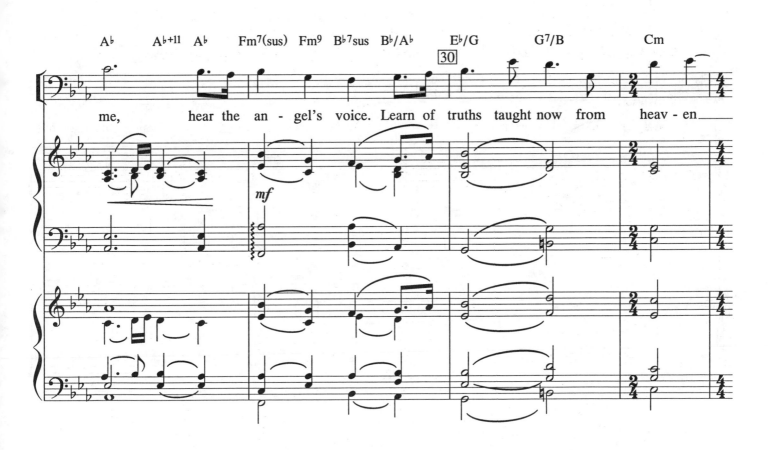

and what's soon to be, go with me.

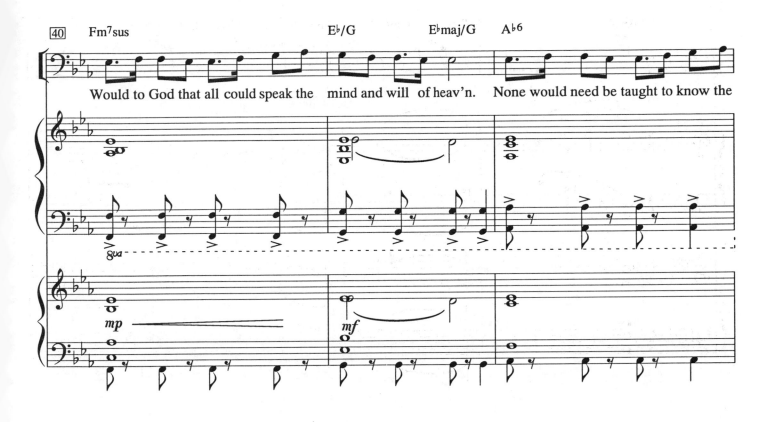

Would to God that all could speak the mind and will of heav'n. None would need be taught to know the

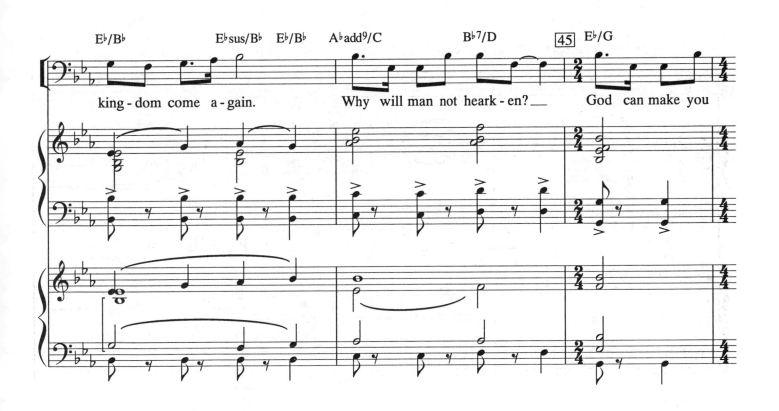

king-dom come a-gain. Why will man not heark-en?__ God can make you

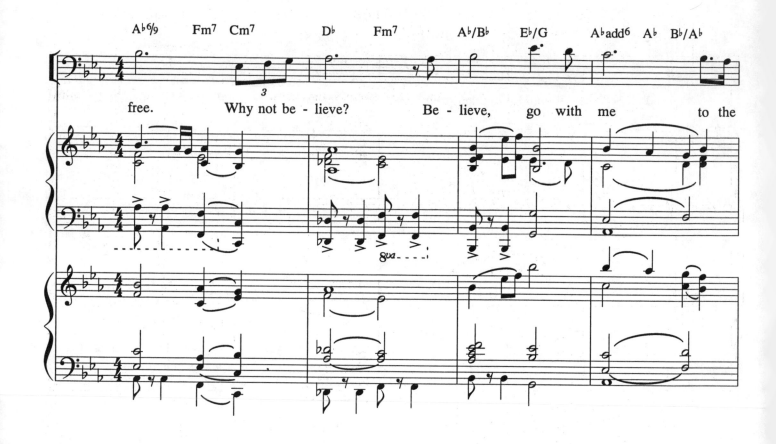

free.   Why not be-lieve?   Be-lieve,   go with me   to the

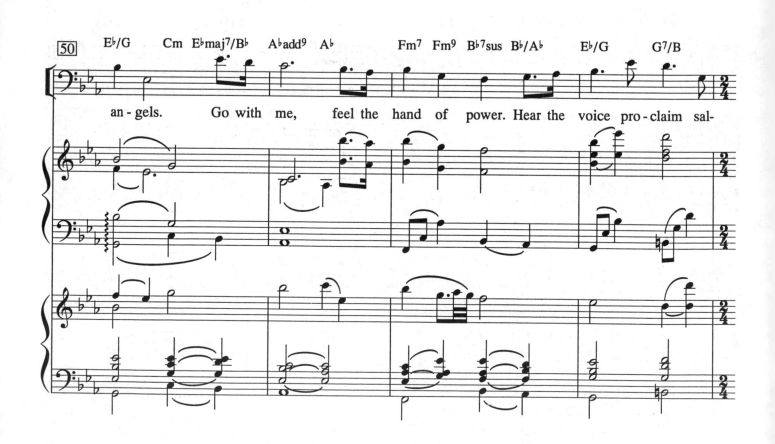

an-gels.   Go with me,   feel the hand of power. Hear the voice pro-claim sal-

Taste the love of heav - en, yes, come and see. Come and see._____

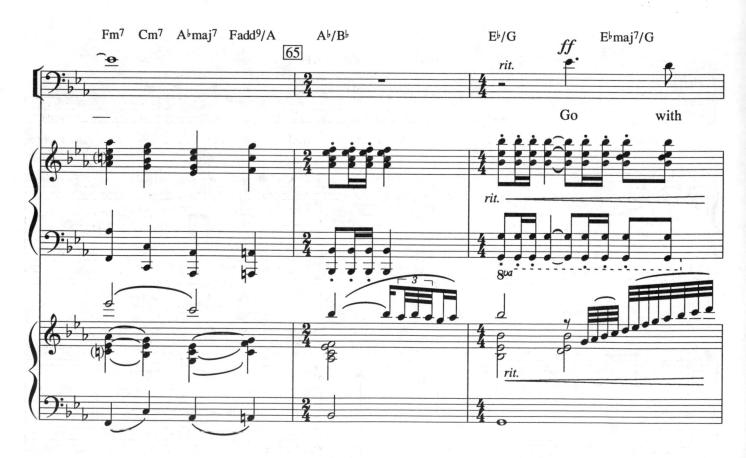

Go with

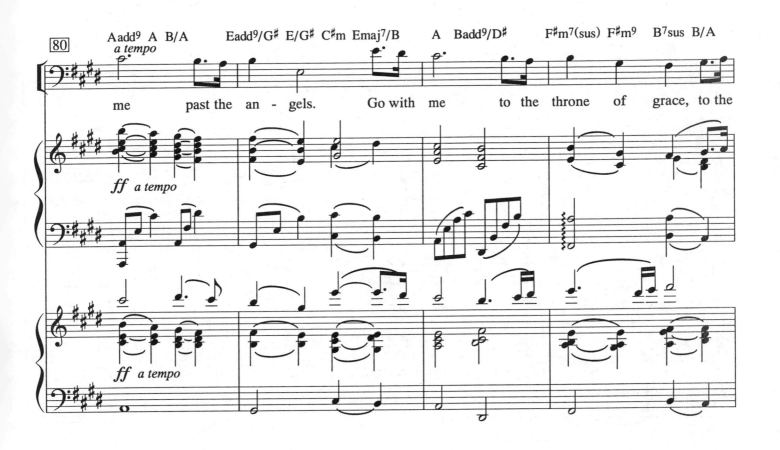

49

50

GOING AS A LAMB

Arranged by
RANDY KARTCHNER

Words and Music by
KENNETH COPE

52

JOSEPH III: Fa - ther, oh fa - ther, why can't you stay __ with us? Fa - ther, dear fa - ther, must they

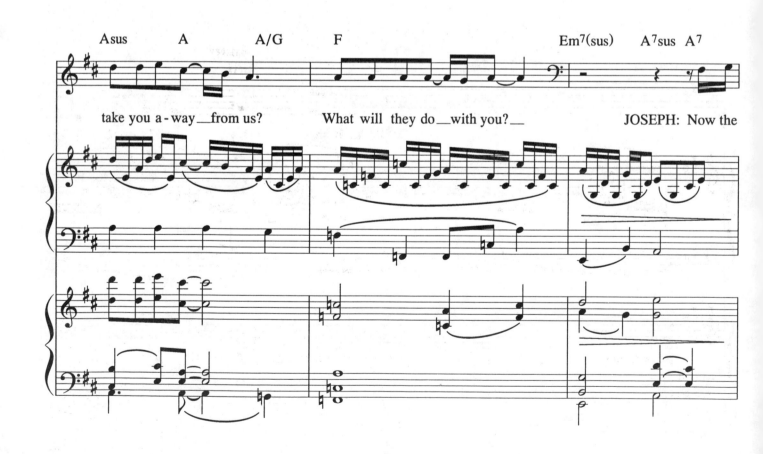

take you a - way __ from us? What will they do __ with you? __ JOSEPH: Now the

sword is drawn, and I can't look on. I am go-ing as a lamb.

EMMA: If they slay you Jo-seph, I am

56

MAN OF SORROWS

Arranged by
RANDY KARTCHNER

Words and Music by
KENNETH COPE

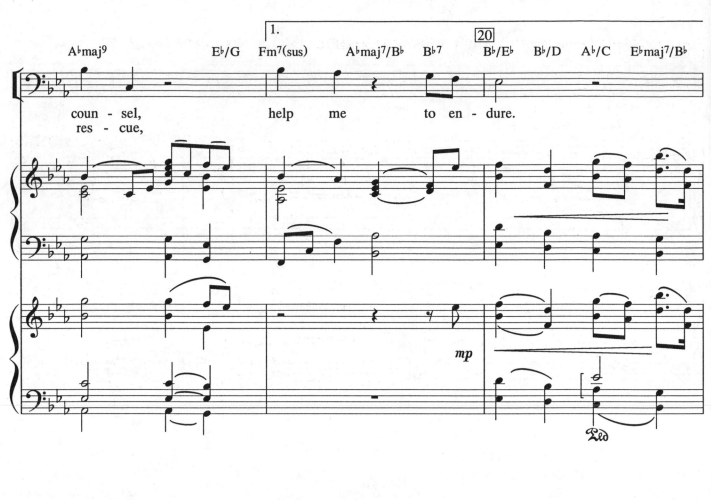

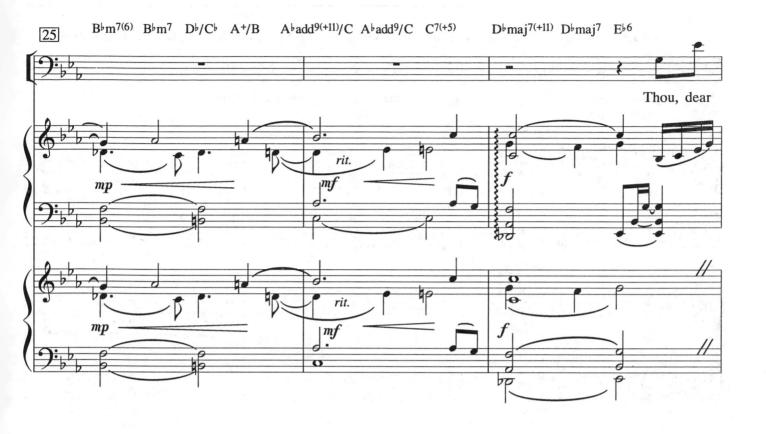

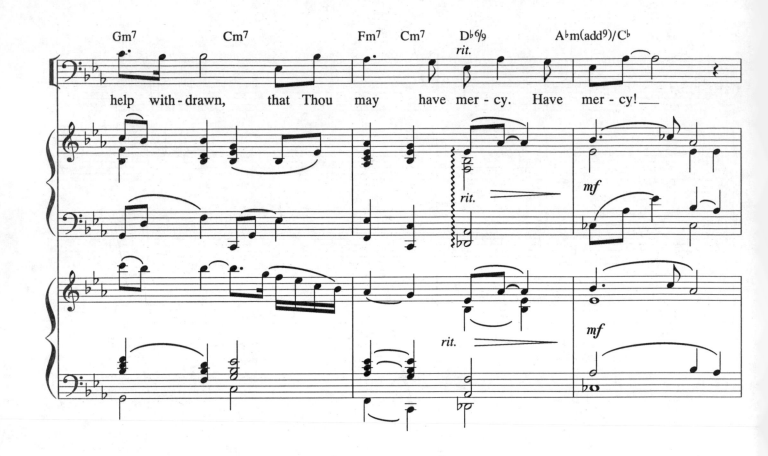

help with-drawn, that Thou may have mer - cy. Have mer - cy!___

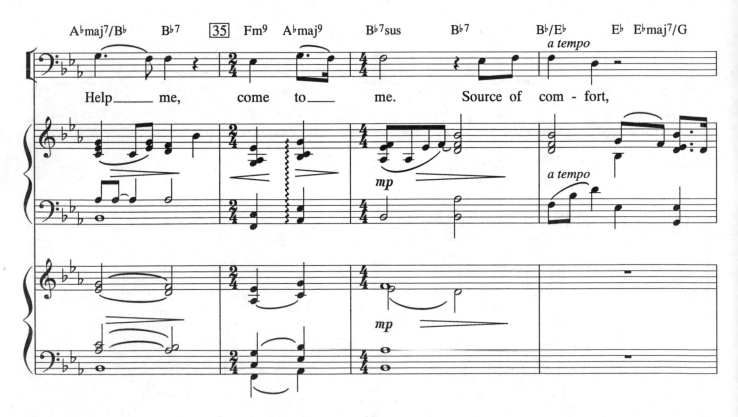

Help___ me, come to___ me. Source of com - fort,

64

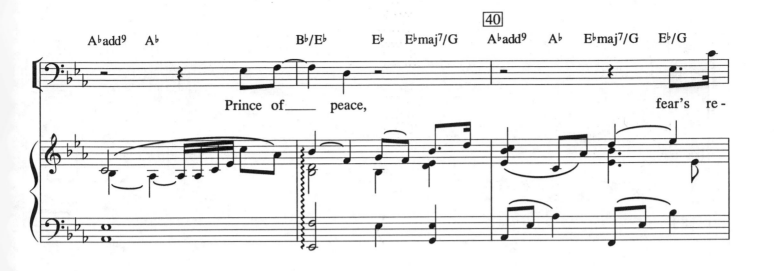

Prince of____ peace,

fear's re-

lief,

faith's re-ward.

I am____

66

whole.____ Man of sor - rows, Je - sus, take me home.____

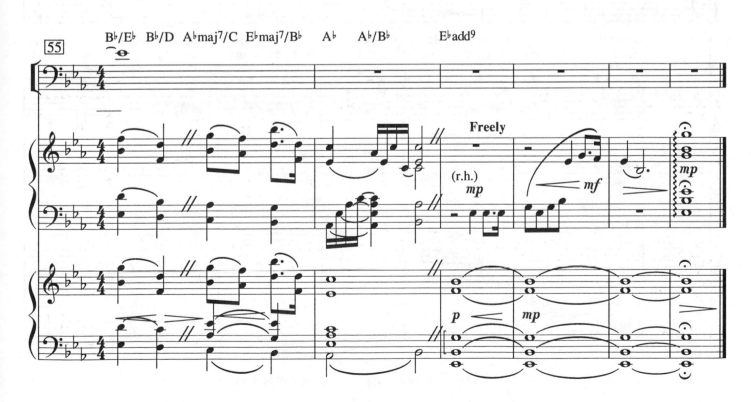

67

BROTHERS

Arranged by
RANDY KARTCHNER

Words and Music by
KENNETH COPE

70

nev - er to fade,___ wheth - er near___ or far.___ Broth - ers in___ life,___

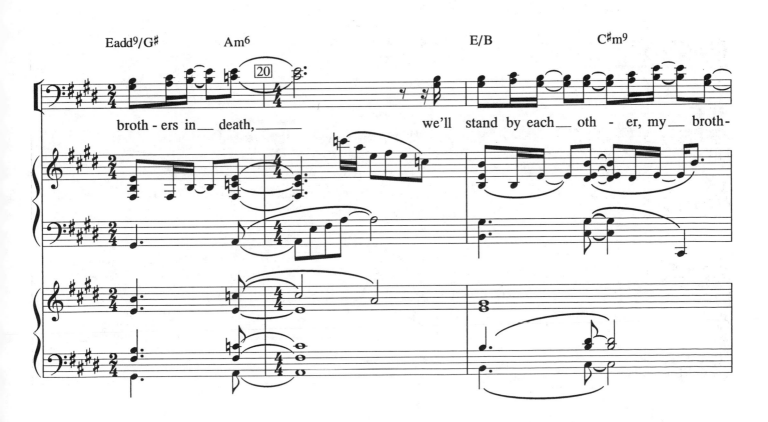

broth - ers in___ death,_____ we'll stand by each___ oth - er, my___ broth-

er, through now___ and the end.___

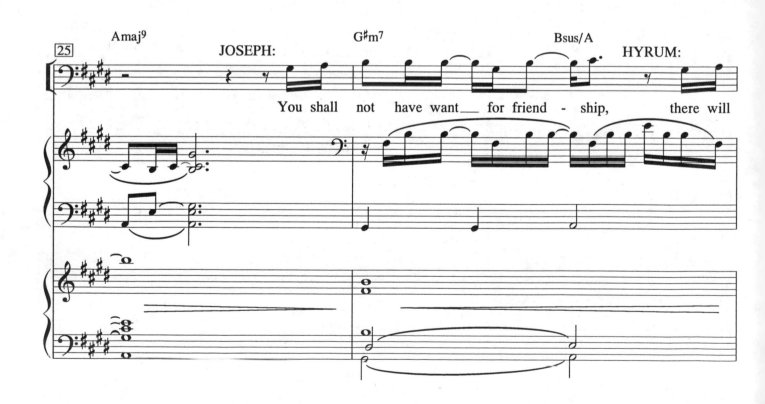

JOSEPH:

You shall not have want___ for friend - ship,

HYRUM:

there will

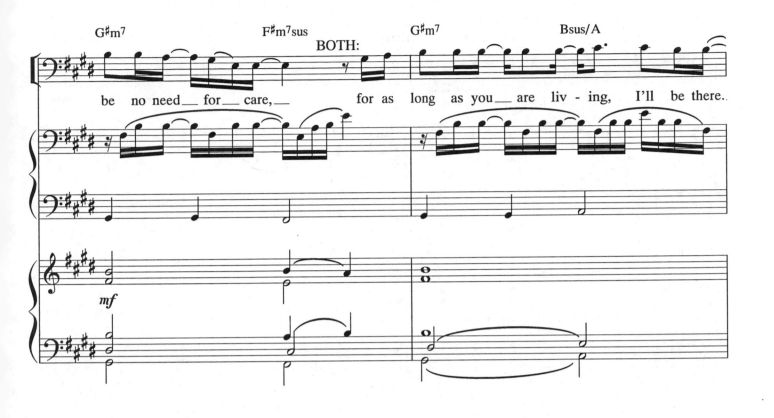

be no need___ for___ care,___ for as long as you___ are liv - ing, I'll be there.

I'll go with you in - to pri - son, I'll go

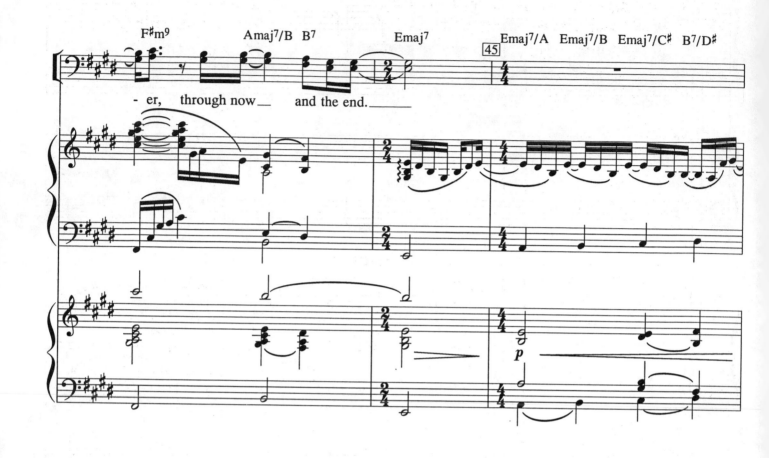

- er, through now___ and the end.___

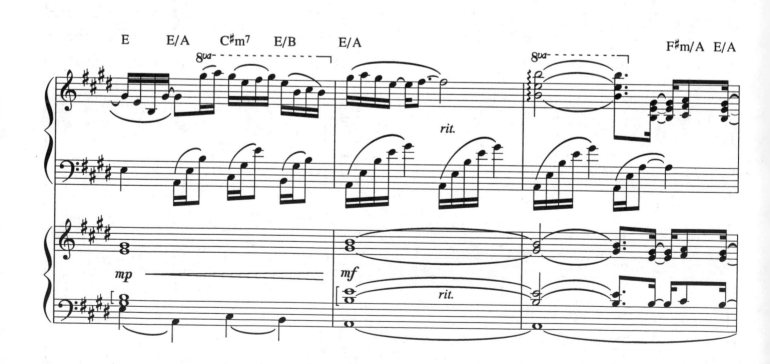

WHY MUST THE GOOD DIE/FREE AT LAST

Arranged by
RANDY KARTCHNER

Words and Music by
KENNETH COPE

Chords above first system: A♭maj7 A♭ Fm7 E♭add9/G G♭maj13 C♭maj7 A♭m/C♭ A♭maj7/B♭ G(-9)/B G7/B

Rehearsal mark: 10

Lyrics: way,_____ a - way, tak - en a - way,_____

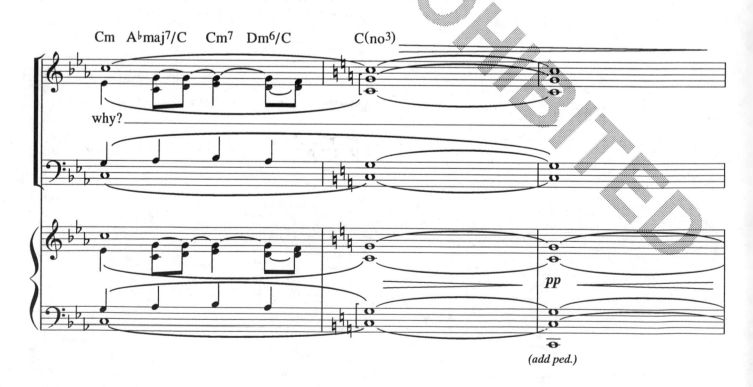

Chords above second system: Cm A♭maj7/C Cm7 Dm6/C C(no3)_____

Lyrics: why?_____

pp

(add ped.)

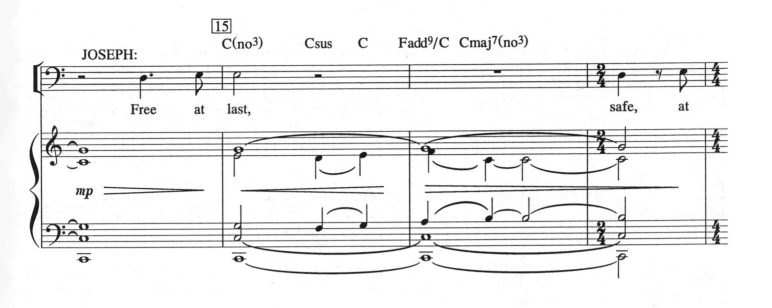

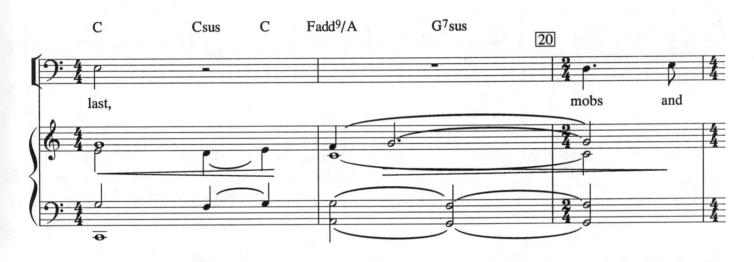

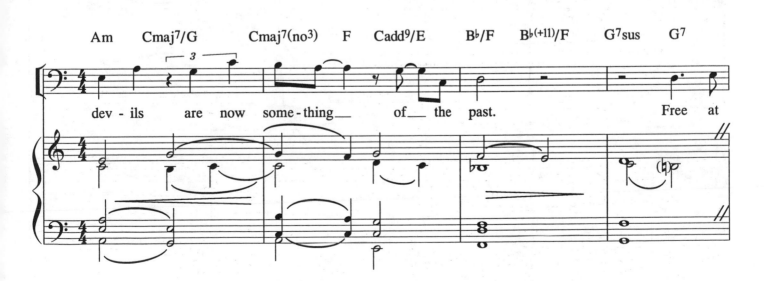

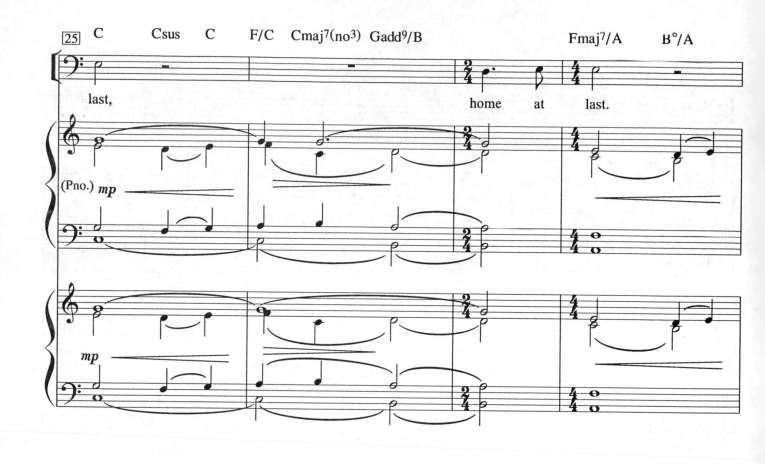

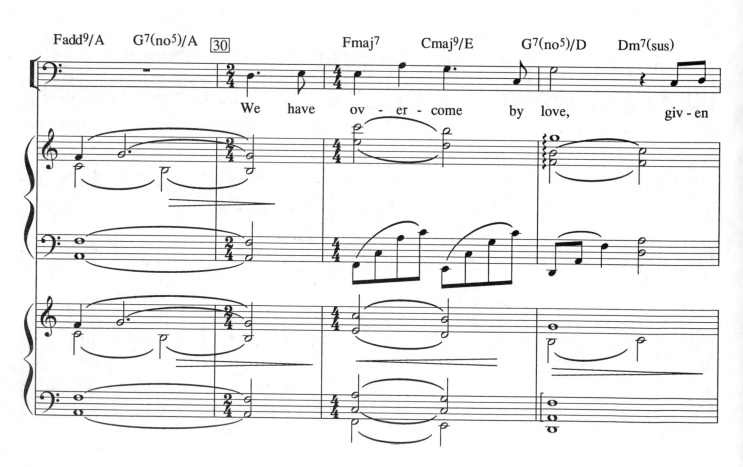

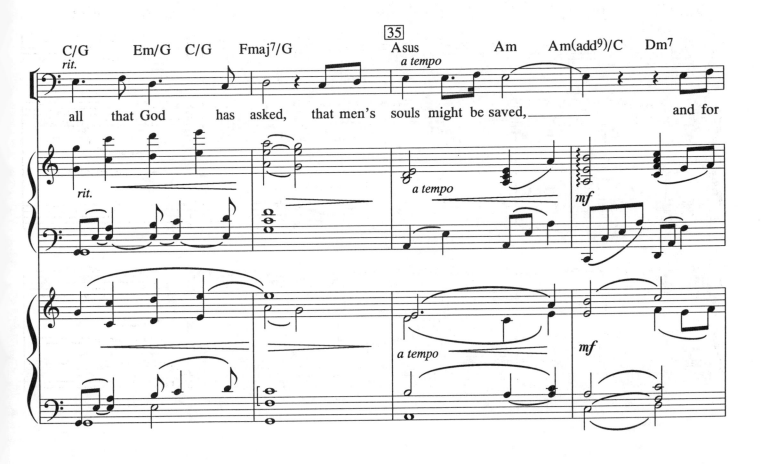

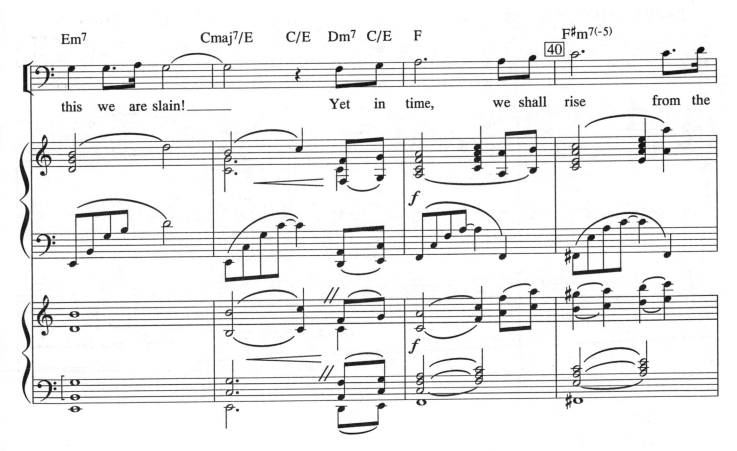

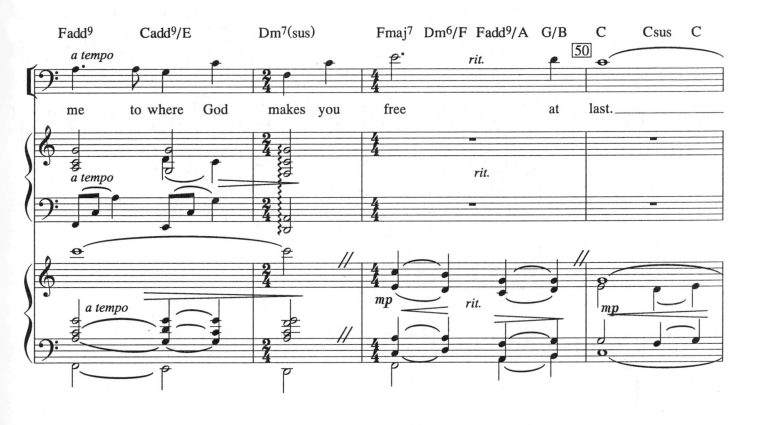

Fadd⁹   Cadd⁹/E   Dm⁷(sus)   Fmaj⁷ Dm⁶/F Fadd⁹/A G/B   C   Csus   C

me   to where God   makes you   free   at   last.

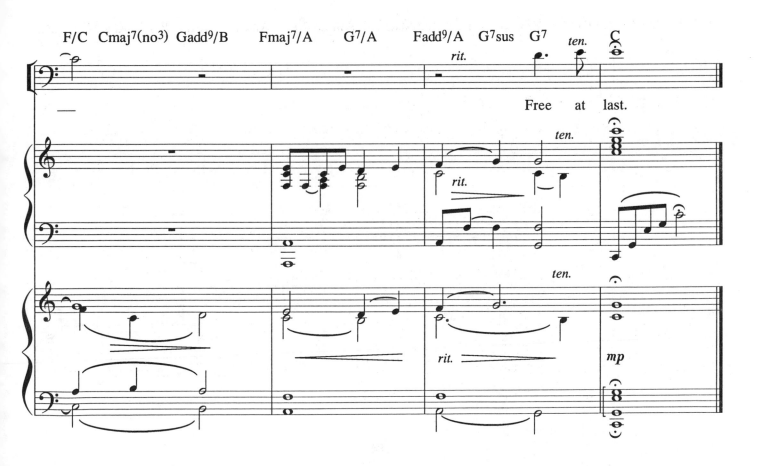

F/C Cmaj⁷(no³) Gadd⁹/B   Fmaj⁷/A   G⁷/A   Fadd⁹/A G⁷sus G⁷

Free   at   last.

COME, FOLLOW ME

(Melody: "A Poor Wayfaring Man of Grief")

Words by
KENNETH COPE
Arranged by
RANDY KARTCHNER

Music Adapted by
KENNETH COPE
Melody by
GEORGE COLES (1792-1858)

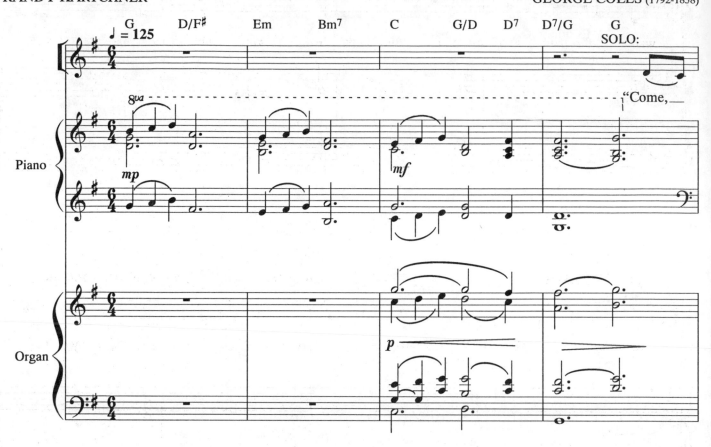

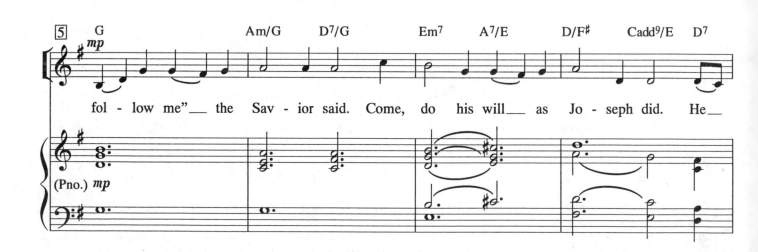

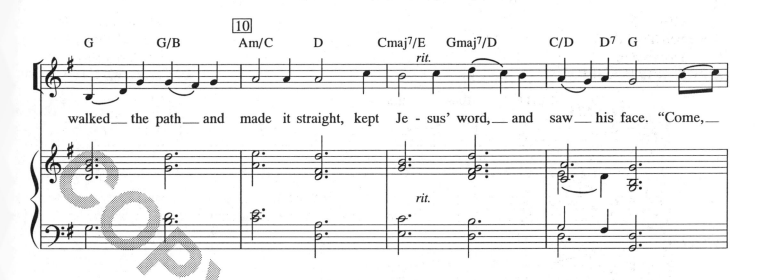

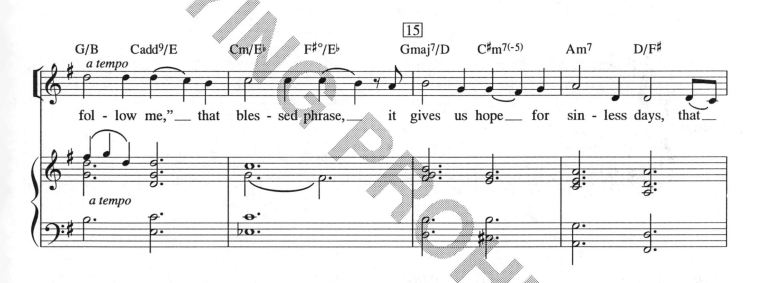

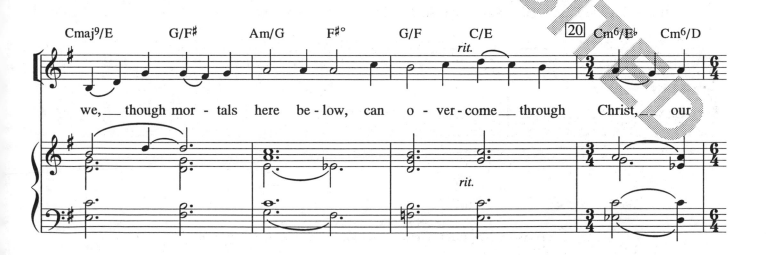

an - swer be,___ how well thou heard___ "Come, fol - low me."

Come, fol - low me,___ come, fol - low me.